Who's coming?

Who should Baby Shark invite to his party? Colour in his friends so he can invite them!

Clam buns!

Grandpa Shark has made some of his famous clam buns for the party. How many has he made?

Party time!

Baby Shark is planning a party. Can you decorate his party hat for him?

Party time!

Baby Shark is planning a party. Can you decorate his party hat for him?

Decorations!

Mummy Shark has lots of lovely decorations for the party. Colour in the flags, blue, orange, pink and green!

Music!

Daddy Shark is in charge of the music for the party. What instruments can you see?

Get ready!

Everyone is wearing their very best clothes for the party. Who do you think looks the smartest?

Baby Whale

Here's Baby Whale! He has a present for Baby Shark. What do you think it is?

Baby Turtle

Next to arrive is Baby Turtle. She's brought a cake. It looks yummy! How many strawberries can you see on it?

William

Now William is here and the party can start. He's brought their friend Big Whale.

Party!

Baby Shark loves to play games with his friends. Can you find them all?

Yummy food!

There is lots of lovely food to eat at the party.
What would you choose?

Sandcastles

Grandma Shark has challenged
Baby Shark and his friends
to build a sandcastle.
Who has built the biggest one?

Music

Baby Shark and his family have a surprise. They are going to play some music. What do you think they'll play?

'Doo-doo-doo-doo-doo-doo!'

Dancing

Everyone is dancing
and having fun.
It's a great party.
Can you dance too?

Sleepy!

Everyone is tired from all the dancing. Who is going to have a rest?

Fish Bus!

Baby Shark has another surprise for his friends.
A ride in Fish Bus! Where do you think they'll go?

Hammerhead Shark!

They have gone to visit Hammerhead Shark! He's very pleased to see them. Baby Shark has taken him a clam bun!

Swimming race!

They all swim back to the others. Who do you think will win and get there first?

FINISH

The winner!

Daddy Shark has a special prize for the winner. It's a gold cup!

Cake time!

Now it's time to eat Baby Turtle's delicious cake. What type of cake do you think it is?

Dressing up!

Mummy Shark has a fun game to play. She has lots of costumes to dress up in. Everyone has to guess who they are.

Grandma Shark and Grandpa Shark!

Who have Grandma Shark
and Grandpa Shark
dressed up as?

Mummy Shark and Daddy Shark!

Who have Mummy Shark and Daddy Shark dressed up as?

Baby Shark!

Baby Shark goes last.
Who has he dressed
up as?

Shark Family Orchestra!

The Shark Family Orchestra have one last surprise. They are going to play a special song for all the guests.

Friends!

Baby Shark is happy. He loves
having a party with his friends.

Balloons

Baby Shark has got a balloon for each of his friends. How many balloons is he holding?

One for you!

Baby Whale has got a balloon. What colour do you think it should be?

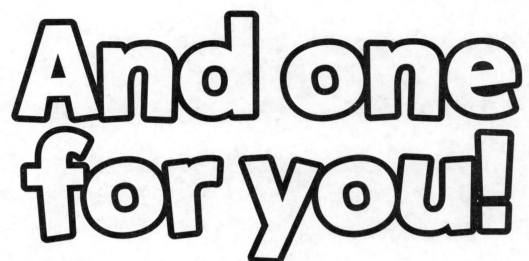

And one for you!

Next to get a
balloon is Baby
Turtle. What
colour do you
think hers
should be?

One for William

William's got
a balloon now.
Can you colour it to
match the colour
orange he is?

Thank you!

It's time to say goodbye to Baby Shark.

See you next time.